beyond measure

conversations across art and science

Kettle's Yard, University of Cambridge

Acknowledgments

We would like to thank all the artists and contributors to this exhibition, and to those involved in the many related workshops and events.

We would also like to thank the following people, who in many various ways, have helped us to realise this project:

Claire Abrahams
Elisabeth Andersson, TATE Conservation
Charles Asprey
Jade Awdry, Haunch of Venison
Jacqui Barouch
Karen Bates
Lucy Blaxland, Museum of the History of Science, University of Oxford
Browse & Darby Gallery
Marie Bjerrum
Alex Bradley & Craig Burnett, White Cube Gallery
Prof. Andrew Brewerton
Ben Brown
Stuart Bull
John Butcher
Tristram Carfrae
Peter Carl
Anika Carpenter, Nick Dowdeswell and Richard Wadhams, KT Projects
Prof. Michael Carpenter
Frank Clark
Phil Clarke
Rosa and Carlos de la Cruz
Edith Devaney
Graham Dolan
Joanne Edwards
Robert Egan
Prof. Stuart Elden
Jennifer Evans
Annette Faux
Robert Fiegel
Alice Foster
Elena Ochoa Foster, Ivory Press
Colin and Carole Fraser
Carl Freedman, Carl Freedman Gallery
Jim Godfrey
Prof. Jeremy Gray
Spencer de Grey
Thomas Hanbury, Dicksmith Gallery
Trent Hare
Claude Heath
Andrew Herdon, Karolin Kober and Justyna Niewiara, Lisson Gallery
Mark Hoelzer
Ruth Horry
Clare Hostombe
Mark Hurn
Jill Ivatts
Paul Janew
Jeffrey R. Johnson

Margaret Johnston
Branwen Jones, Andrea Rosen Gallery
David Juda, Nina Fellmann and Laura Henderson, Annely Juda Fine Art
Irene Kightley
Frank King
Geoffrey Kolbe
Xavier De Kostelier
Prof. Sir Harry Kroto
George L-Legendre
Mike Lewis
Prof. Peter Littlewood
Prof. Malcolm Longair
Katie McInnes
Prof. Benoit Mandelbrot
Gillian Marston
Jessica Mastro, Castelli Gallery
Keith Moore, The Royal Society
Sean Moulton
Eva Nicolas-Amoros
Prof. James Norris
Allen Packwood
Brady Peters
Michelle Reyes, The Felix Gonzalez-Torres Foundation
Prof. Carol Robinson
Maria Rollo, The Science Museum
Karl Sandeman
Rosemary Saunders
Anne Schwanz, Eigen + Art Leipzig/Berlin
Michelle Scurll
Kristina Shea
Annette Shelford
Victor Skipp
Stephen Snoddy
Kate Spence
Phil Stickler
Peter Stubley
Tao Sule
Emma Sutton
Liba Taub, the Whipple Museum of the History and Philosophy of Science
Anne Taylor
Prof. Burt Totaro
Dalibor Vesely
Prof. Sir David and Lady Elizabeth Wallace
Helen Waters, Alan Cristea Gallery
Veryan Weston
Gary Woodley
Mick Young
Marcus Ritter and Kate Zamet, Ritter/Zamet Gallery

The Fellowship of Churchill College
Churchill Archives Centre

Beyond Measure

Place

Beyond Measure is an exhibition in which the artist's studio, scientist's laboratory and writer's study are explored on the basis of a common concept that reaches across different disciplines. Throughout the exhibition the aim is to encourage conversations among highly specialised works by mathematicians, scientists, architects, artists and designers. The gallery itself opens up as a place of experimentation, a 'working place', in which the exhibits are themselves 'works in progress'. Drawing from distinct yet interrelated domains, the exhibition highlights complex scientific and artistic investigations, and the contexts and possibilities of the places where knowledge and culture are made.

This notion of the interrelated nature of places of imagination and experimentation is rooted in the simple assertion that 'things happen somewhere'. Yet, this relation to the 'somewhere', the specific place in which something happens, has undergone a subtle though profound transformation over the course of history, a transformation in parallel with the development of geometry.

To qualify this remark, let us reflect for a moment, on the history of geometry.

The word itself is derived from the Greek *geos* – meaning earth and *metron* – meaning measure. However, scholars tell us that geometry was introduced not by the Greeks, but by the Egyptians, from whom the Ancient Greeks inherited this study. Each year the Nile would flood its banks, covering the land and obliterating the orderly marking of plot and farm areas. This annual flood symbolised to the Egyptian the cyclic return of the primal watery chaos, and, when the waters receded, the work began of redefining and re-establishing the boundaries. Each year the areas would shift according to the temple astronomer who would say that certain celestial configurations had changed so that the orientation or location of a temple had to be adjusted, accordingly reorientating the plots around it. So the laying of the squares upon the earth had, for the Egyptian, a metaphysical as well as a physical and social boundary. This activity of 'measuring the earth' became the basis for a science of natural law as it is embodied in the archetypal forms of the circle, square and triangle, and was seen as the re-establishment of the principle of order and law on earth.

Whilst the historical trajectory of geometry as a branch of mathematics will not be developed here, it is sufficient to say that Euclidean geometry continued to be central to ancient and succeeding societies and was used for surveying, astronomy, and architecture.

Yet, the development of geometry, which began as a collection of empirically discovered principles concerning lengths, angles, areas, and volumes, gave rise to the notion of a singular homogenous space. The consequence of this was that it erased the notion of places, under the idealisation of an 'absolute' space. This erasure has, of course, had consequences beyond the innovations of mathematics and physics, and is central to the contemporary situation in which we find ourselves, and that we have inherited as a consequence of that tradition.

Space

Beyond Measure unfolds out of a question that continues to haunt our modern age: of how we can bridge the divide between the specialised vocabularies of the sciences and arts and audiences outside those specialities. The question itself has its own, well-documented history. However, the urgency of the question remains and informs the cultural context in which this exhibition is presented. It is brought about by the bifurcation of the spaces of science and the everyday places of the world, which is implicit within the rise of geometry.

As stated above, classical science is based on a clear distinction between space and the everyday world of situations and places. The key concept of an absolute space refers to a uniform medium in which things are arranged in three dimensions and in which they remain the same regardless of the position they occupy. In contrast, the everyday world is the world revealed to us by our senses.

At first sight, the everyday world seems to be the one we know best of all, for there is no need either to measure or calculate in order to access this world; we can simply open our eyes and get on with our lives. Yet, we have come to hold developments in the sciences, and science in general, in such high esteem that our lived experience can seem illusional and indistinct. For instance, if you want to know what light is, is it not the physicist who will tell you what it 'really' is? Is light, as once was thought, a stream of burning projectiles, or, as others thought, an energy that emanates from one's own eyes and illuminates objects in the world? Or is it, as modern theory maintains, a phenomenon that can be classed alongside other forms of electromagnetic radiation? Of course, it is the latter that we take for granted to be the accurate account and explanation, even though many of us will not know what electromagnetic radiation is.

If we have the fundamental laws and truths of science, why should we linger over what works of art, and the artists who create them, seem to say? What can they have to tell us about light, colours, reflections and sensations? For it has been suggested that only methodical scientific investigations – using measurements and experiments – can free us from the delusions of our senses and allow us to understand how things really are.

In addressing this question, a number of modern philosophers have responded by claiming that a central task of scientific thinking in the modern era has been to find ways of legitimately describing worldly phenomena in precise terms so that they might be made the subject of exact measurement, statistical analysis, or similar. This necessarily involves a leap from the 'morphological' to the exact – what Edmund Husserl referred to as 'idealisation' while pointing out that:

The world that we actually inhabit contains no geometrical idealities, no geometrical space or mathematical time withal their shapes.

Therefore, exact concepts only ever describe pure possibilities and never actualities. Every act of mathematical description entails a substitution of an ideality for a reality. For example, instead of measuring the area of a roughly rectangular floor, one compromises and works out the area of an idealised rectangle whose exact measurements approximate the actual floor. What one is measuring is not the real floor *per se* but the ideal rectangle that one superimposes on it through mathematical thinking. This process can sometimes be ridiculously artificial; for instance, think of a psychological test that asks you to convert your emotional response to some event into a number between 0 and 10. The translation from morphological concepts (i.e. 'I found the event disturbing and repugnant') to calculable concepts (e.g. the numbers of the scale) often sacrifices a great deal in order to have the 'data' in a manageable form.

The world of science is thus unlike the world of actual experience. The process of 'idealisation', whereby scientific thinking moves to transcend the domain of morphological realities in favour of idealised descriptions, is at the heart of the modern scientific conception of the world, philosophers tell us. What then of the realm of actual experience, which is encountered in the first-person, and has come to be regarded as a 'mere veil of appearances' behind which stands the hidden objective world accessible only to science?

It is often suggested that art has nothing to say, and that modern artists peddle mere perceptions in place of actuality. But what, for instance, can a work like 'Wooden Boulder' by David Nash tell us about forms of time related to the environment in which we live and in which we organise our day-to-day activities?

It is not our intention to deny the value of science, either as a means of technological advancement or insofar as it offers an object lesson on precision and truth. If we wish to learn how to prove something, to conduct thorough investigation or to be critical of preconceptions, it remains entirely appropriate, now as then, that we should turn to science. Moreover, as Maurice Merleau-Ponty wrote in 'The World of Perception':

The question that modern philosophy has asked in relation to science seems not to be whether science does, or ever could, present us with a picture of the world which is complete, self-sufficient and somehow closed in upon itself, such that there could no longer be any meaningful questions outside this picture. It is not a matter of limiting or denying the extent of scientific knowledge, but establishing whether it is entitled to deny or rule out all forms of enquiry that do not start out from measurements and comparisons. This is not a question asked out of hostility to science, far from it, it is science itself – particularly in its most recent developments – which forces the question and which encourages an answer to the negative.

Reconciliation

As a universal tool for stabilising meaning, geometry changed fundamentally with the introduction of non-Euclidean geometry, and with that the idea of an absolute space has undergone a spectacular transformation. The classical concept of a singular unified space has been split into several 'spaces'. Non-Euclidean geometry now considers manifolds, spaces that are considerably more abstract, yet strangely more familiar than Euclidean space, which they only approximately resemble at small scales. Modern geometry has multiple strong bonds with physics. Thus, the language of Riemannian geometry proved to be crucial in general relativity, substituting the former idea of lumps of matter in a three-dimensional space, with a series of events in a four-dimensional space-time. One of the newest physical theories, string theory, is also very geometric in understanding and thinks in anything from ten or eleven (M-theories) to twenty-six dimensions (Bosonic string theories).

The contemporary scientist, unlike his or her predecessor working within the classical paradigm, no longer fosters the illusion that he or she is penetrating to the heart of the object 'as it is in itself'. The mathematical physics of relativity confirms that absolute and final objectivity is a mere illusion by showing how each particular observation is strictly linked to the observer and cannot be abstracted from this particular situation; it also rejects the notion of an absolute observer – and this has had radical ramifications for the presentation of art in the ideal, white cube gallery space. We can no longer flatter ourselves with the idea that in science – as in the arts – the exercise of pure and unsituated intellect can allow us to gain access to the object free of all human traces. This does not render the need for scientific research any less pressing; in fact, the only thing under attack is the dogmatism of specialised practice that thinks itself capable of absolute and complete knowledge. What modern philosophy appears to be implying is simply the need to do justice to each of the various elements of human experience.

Someone recently suggested that, in order to reverse, or at least counter, the estrangement of modern science, or, indeed, any specialised practice, what is needed is a form of enquiry that seeks to rediscover the origins or roots of the scientific disciplines from whence their legitimacy springs. The only way to remedy what has been referred to as 'the crisis of the European sciences' is to rediscover the rootedness of the sciences in the everyday world. Beyond Measure, in a small way, attempts to start out on that journey by bridging different forms of representation in the hope of finding common ground, or even the common place.

Barry Phipps

Plates

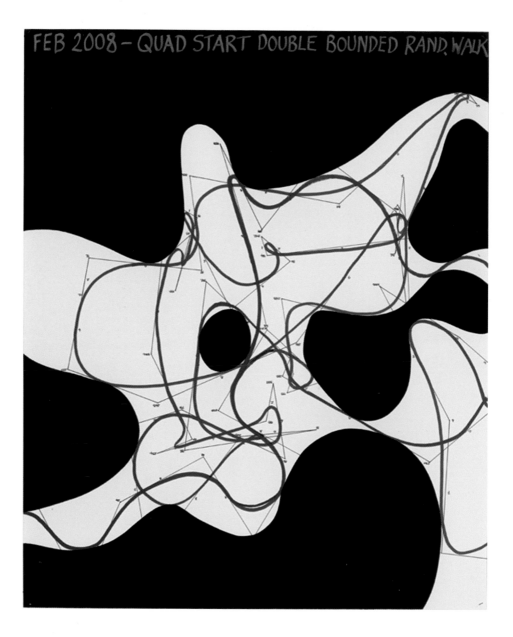

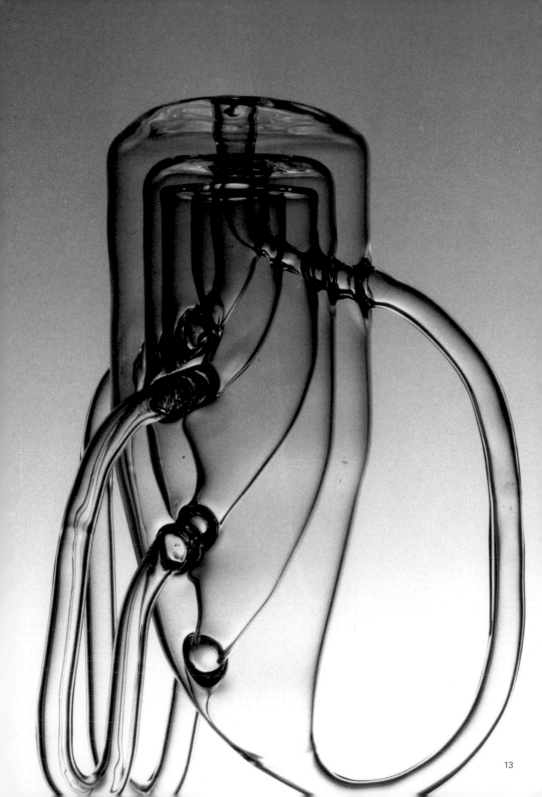

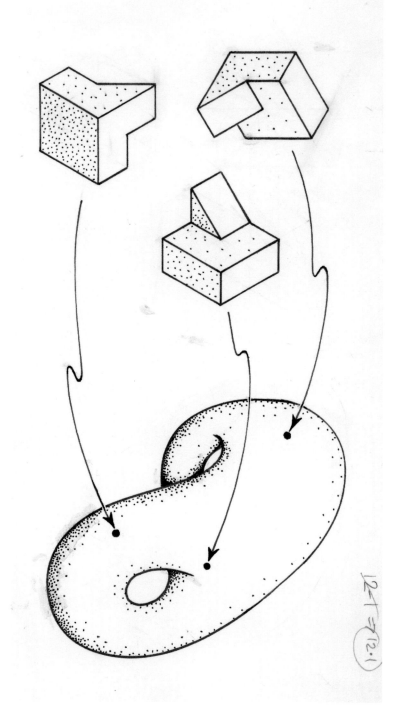

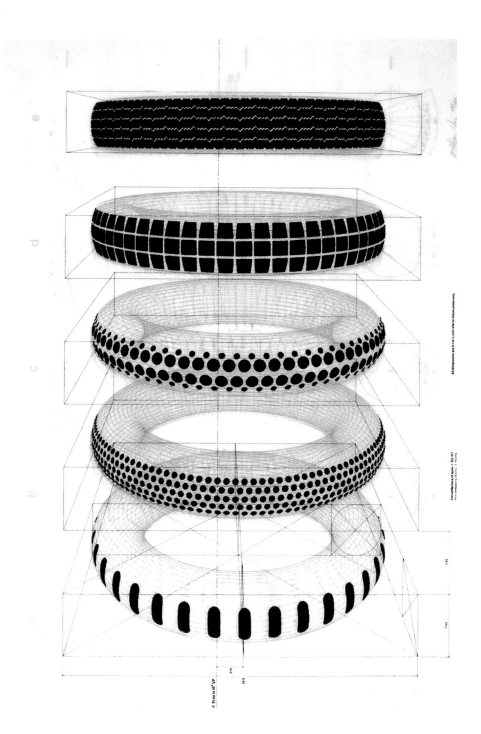

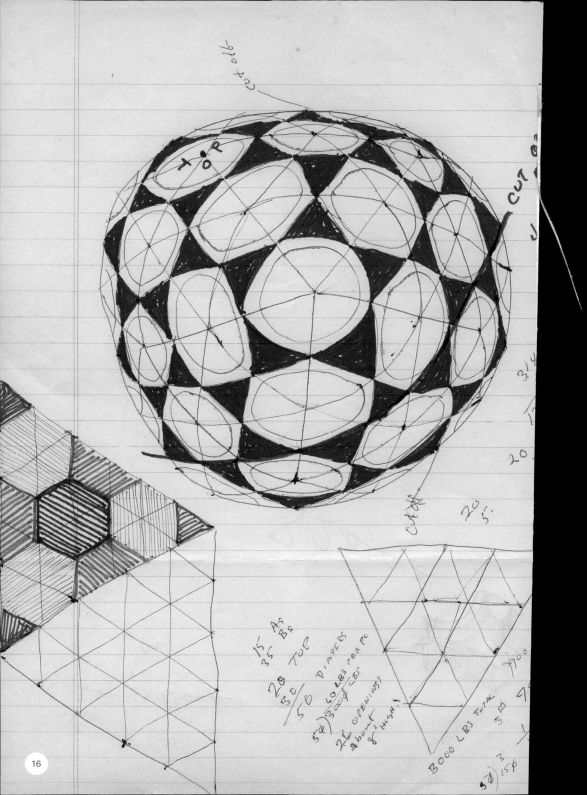

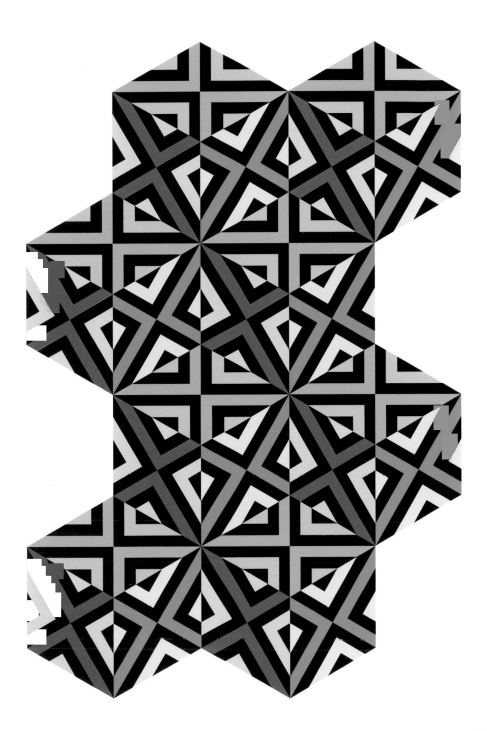

Cones

If you slice a cone you get one of four possible mathematical curves depending at what angle you make the slice. They correspond to possible orbits.

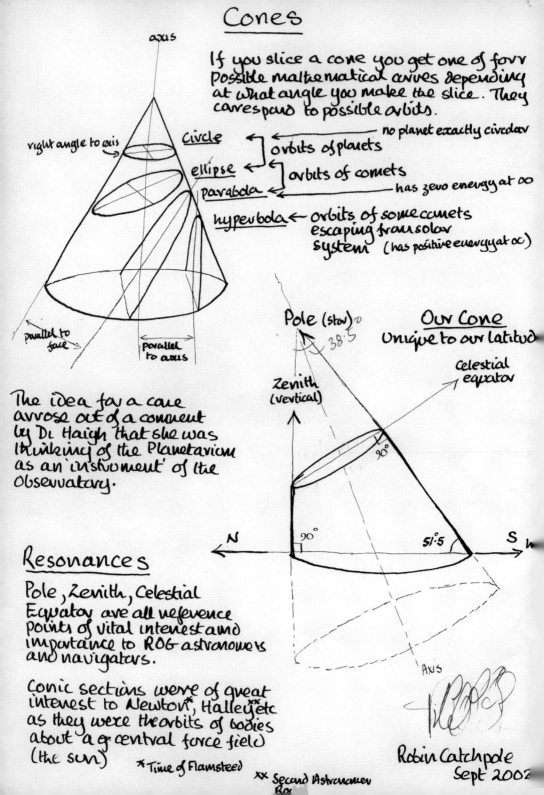

axis

right angle to axis — **Circle** ← ——— no planet exactly circular
— orbits of planets
ellipse ← — orbits of comets
parabola ← ——— has zero energy at ∞
hyperbola ← orbits of some comets escaping from solar system (has positive energy at ∞)

parallel to face

parallel to axis

The idea for a cone arose out of a comment by Dr Haigh that she was thinking of the Planetarium as an 'instrument' of the Observatory.

Our Cone
Unique to our latitude

Pole (star) — 38.5

Zenith (vertical)

Celestial equator

90°

N — 90° — 51.5 — S

Axis

Resonances

Pole, Zenith, Celestial Equator are all reference points of vital interest and importance to ROG astronomers and navigators.

Conic sections were of great interest to Newton*, Halley** etc as they were the orbits of bodies about a g central force field (the sun)

* Time of Flamsteed

** Second Astronomer Roy

Robin Catchpole
Sept 2002

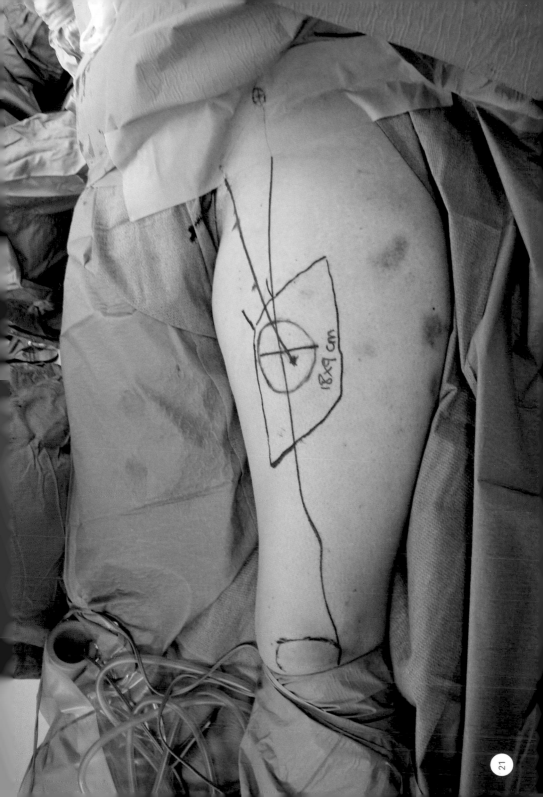

18 x 9 cm

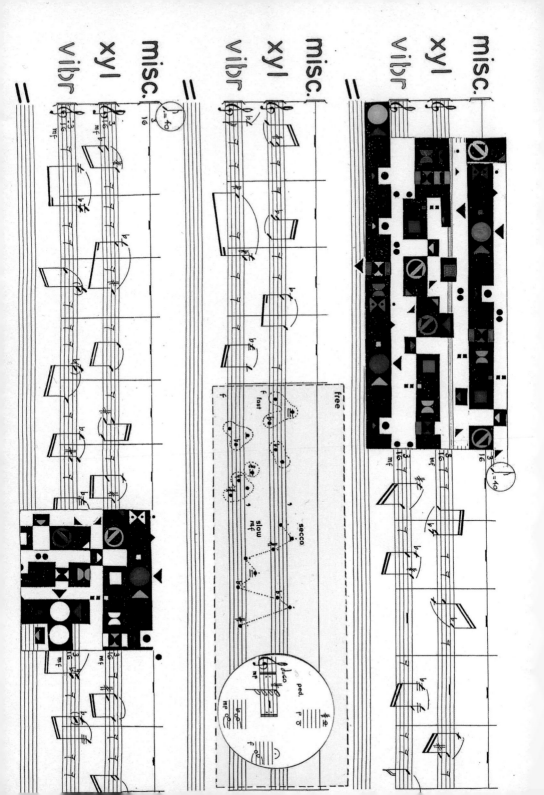

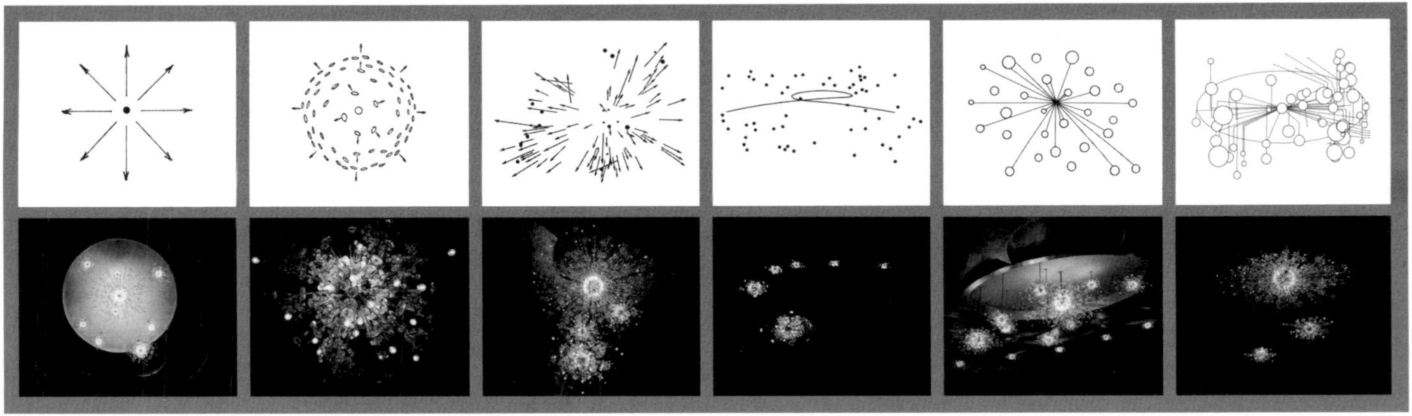

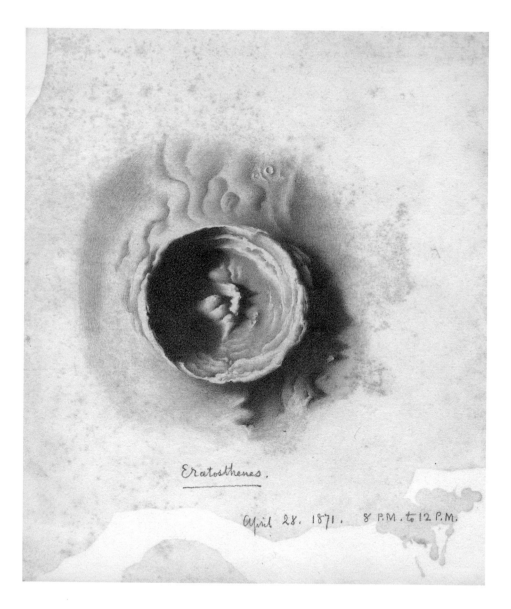

Eratosthenes.

April 28. 1871. 8 P.M. to 12 P.M.

Modified icosahedra

1	4	4
2	6	12
10	5	50

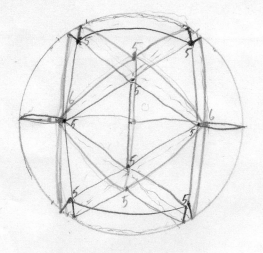

1	3
3	6
9	5

3	4	12
4	6	24
6	5	

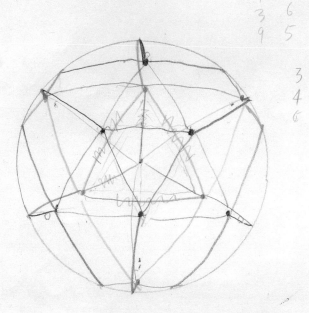

29

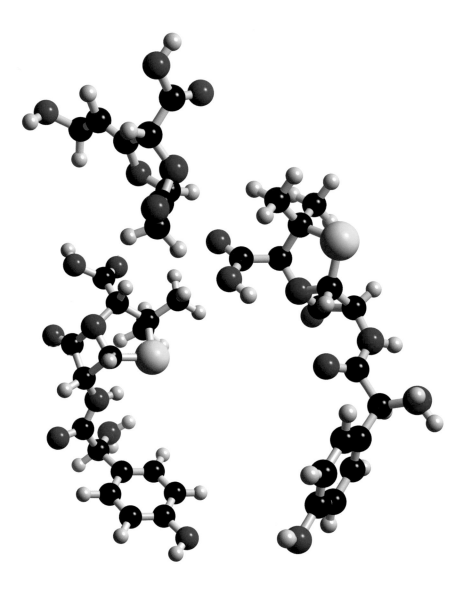

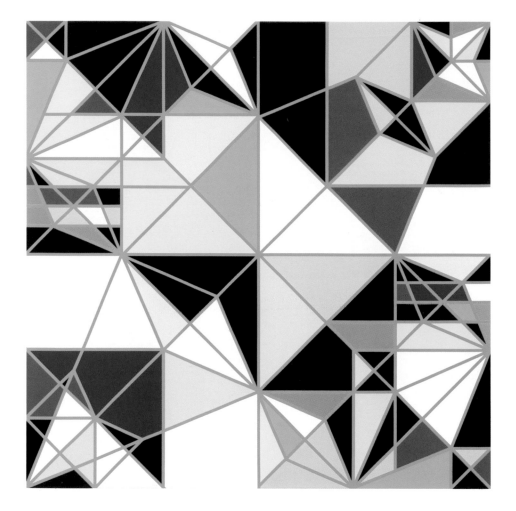

List of Illustrations

cover:
studio with three steel models
House, 2006, *Jewel*, 2006, *Another Mountain*, 2007
RICHARD DEACON

inside cover:
Air Routes of Britain (Day), 2000
Air Routes of Britain (Night), 2000
LANGLANDS & BELL
Courtesy the artists and Alan Cristea Gallery

plates:

p 9
Model of glassy metal alloys, 1977
Dr PHIL GASKELL
*Courtesy of the Cavendish Laboratory,
University of Cambridge*

pp 10, 11
Ball and spoke model of the crystal structure
of Chlorite
Selected by **STEVE LAURIE**
*Courtesy of Dept. of Earth Sciences,
University of Cambridge*

Amor Intellectualis erga Deum, 2001
(acrylic on canvas)
NADER AHRIMAN
*Collection Charles Asprey /
Klosterfelde Gallery Berlin*

pp 12, 13
*Feb 2008 – Quad Start Double Bounded
Rand Walk*
KEITH TYSON
Courtesy the artist and PaceWildenstein

Klein bottle, 1995
ALAN BENNETT

pp 14, 15
Drawing of configuration space C, each of whose
points represents a possible location of a given
rigid body in Euclidean 3-space E^3: C is a non-
Euclidean 6-manifold, 2006
Prof. Sir ROGER PENROSE

Five Tyres remoulded, 1971 (screenprint)
RICHARD HAMILTON
*Courtesy Alan Cristea Gallery, London
Collection Michael Craig-Martin
© Richard Hamilton. All rights reserved 2008.*

Contributors

Mr Tariq Ahmad, consultant plastic reconstruction and aesthetic surgeon, Addenbrookes Hospital, Cambridge

Plastic surgery is the surgical discipline concerned with reconstruction; the name means to 'refashion' or 'remould'. It is a wide-ranging speciality: we may be involved anywhere in the human body and with a wide spectrum of problems, both in children and adults. Congenital defects, skin, head, neck and breast cancer, trauma such as accidents and burns – whatever the problem, we have developed methods to try to reconstruct tissues with the ethos of 'like for like'. Geometry and topology are core techniques in plastic surgery, facilitating meticulous preoperative planning essential in achieving the optimum outcome for our patients.

Nader Ahriman, artist

Paul Appleton, architect, Allies and Morrison

A new 118 seat planetarium has been inserted in the centre of the Royal Observatory site at Greenwich. The Peter Harrison Planetarium is housed in a cone whose geometry reflects key astronomical concepts in its relation to the space. Above ground this is manifested as a tilted bronze cone aligned with the North Star at 51.5°. The disc, cut at 90° through its apex, is parallel to the celestial equator. This plane is clad in layers of reflecting glass in which the space of the passing sky is revealed.

Dr Francis Archer, structural engineer, ARUP

The Grand Egyptian Museum is a monumental cultural project next to the Pyramids of Giza close to Cairo. It will house and exhibit treasures of Ancient Egypt, which are to be moved from their existing home within the city. Arup are providing structural and facade engineering services as part of a joint venture that includes the architects Heneghan Peng. The key visual element of the building is its wall of stone. The wall is 750m long, 50m tall at its highest point, and composed of over 33,000 framed triangular panels in a series of mathematical fractal patterns.

Dr Miguel de Beistegui, philosopher, University of Warwick

Alan Bennett, glass blower / scientific instrument designer / maker

In mathematics, the Klein bottle is a certain non-orientable surface, i.e., a surface (a two-dimensional topological space) with no distinct 'inner' and 'outer' sides. Other related non-orientable objects include the Möbius strip and the real projective plane. Whereas a Möbius strip is a two dimensional object with one side and one edge, a Klein bottle is a two dimensional object with one side and no edges.

Dr Jim Bennett, historian,
Director of the Museum of the History of Science,
University of Oxford

Dr Christoph Bergemann, quantum physicist,
(formerly) Cavendish Laboratory, University of
Cambridge
Similar to the shell system of atomic orbits that
gives rise to the periodic system of elements,
quantum mechanics dictates that the conducting
electrons in a piece of metal can also take on
only very specific states. Loosely speaking, each
of these quantum states has a well-determined
velocity, i.e. it "lives" in an abstract three-
dimensional momentum space. The Fermi
surfaces pictured here visualize which states
are occupied or empty in several interesting
materials, and many interesting properties of the
material are directly related to the geometry of
these surfaces.

Prof. Sir Tom Blundell, biochemist,
Sir William Dunn Professor of Biochemistry and
Head of the Department of Biochemistry, University
of Cambridge
Ribbon diagrams, also known as Richardson
Diagrams after Jane Richardson, are 3D
schematic representations of protein structure
and are one of the most common methods of
protein depiction used today. Ribbon diagrams
are simple, yet powerful, in expressing the visual
basics of a molecular structure (twist, fold and
unfold). This method has successfully portrayed
the overall organization of the protein structure,
reflecting its 3-dimensional information, and
allowing for better understanding of a complex
object by structural biologists.

Jeff Bryant, computer illustrator, Wolfram Research
String theory predicts the existence of more than
the 3 space dimensions and 1 time dimension we
are all familiar with. According to string theory,
there are additional dimensions that we are
unfamiliar with because they are curled up into
tiny complicated shapes that can only be seen on
tiny scales.

Dr Robin Catchpole, astronomer,
University of Cambridge

Dr Tony Crowther, molecular biologist,
MRC Laboratory of Molecular Biology,
University of Cambridge
Viruses self-assemble with strict geometrical
constraints and the resulting shells often have
icosahedral symmetry. Electron microscopy and
computer processing are used to make three-
dimensional maps, which can be displayed as
density or contours or as cut out models. The
items shown exemplify the different approaches
used for display.

Krysten Cunningham, artist

Richard Deacon, sculptor

Tom Dixon, designer, Creative Director at Artek,
teaches at the Royal College of Art
After dropping out of art school in 1980, Tom
organised warehouse parties before teaching
himself welding. His DIY approach to design
matched the post-punk mood of the early
1980s. Having made his name by making and
selling limited editions of his welded furniture
– such as the Pylon Chair – Dixon continued
his collaborations with other designers, before
becoming head of design at Habitat in 1998.
He continues to initiate new projects as an
independent designer and as creative director of
Artek, the Finnish furniture manufacturer founded
by the architect Alvar Aalto in the 1930s.
"A kind friend once described me as a 'vertebrate
designer'," Dixon said. "That means that I design
from the bones outwards and am not really
interested in surface."

Dr Phil Gaskell, physicist, University of Cambridge
Atoms are perfectly ordered in crystals. Liquids
are completely random. Or are they? Are key
characteristics of the crystal structure retained in
the liquid? Glasses are frozen liquids: easier to
investigate because atoms are stationary. This
structure was built, by hand, to examine whether
glassy metals, newly discovered in the 1970s, are
structurally similar to their crystalline relatives.

Prof. Gerry Gilmore, astronomer, Professor of
Experimental Philosophy, University of Cambridge

Guillermo Gregorio, composer/ musician,
Purdue University
If I were to talk about my own experience,
I could say many things about the strong
impressions that I have received from various
types of music during my life, but I think that the
most important elements acting in my music
come from the visual arts – more specifically,
from the so called "constructive" tendencies of
twentieth-century art, namely, some varieties of
Constructivism and Concrete Art as developed
in Russia and Europe and extended in South
America... What I inherit from Constructive Art
is the opposition to the Romantic aesthetic of
"pure" intuition, inspiration, or the "mystery
of creation" and, ultimately, to the pretension
of placing oneself above historical reality. The
laws I follow are those I have chosen for my
purposes, to solve as best I can certain problems
that I have set for myself. I don't feel burdened
with the metaphysics of earlier artists, and I don't
regard the shapes (or geometry) as mysterious
symbolizing agents.

Dr Peter Grindrod, planetary geologist, University College, London.
Venus: Map of the Aglaonice Region on Venus. This geological map is derived from Synthetic Aperture Radar (SAR) images returned by the NASA Magellan spacecraft in the early 1990s. It covers an area roughly four times that of France. By studying the geological evolution of the area, the map reveals shapes and forms of the features present, including lava flows from coronae (large features apparently unique to Venus) and smaller volcanoes. Courtesy Peter Grindrod, UCL, and Journal of Maps.

Felix Gonzalez-Torres, artist

Dr Simon Guest, engineer, University of Cambridge
Simon Guest works on structures that can deform and change their shape, for example developing deployable structures for use on spacecraft. Geometry plays a central role in his work, understanding how structures fit together, and how they change shape as they deform.

Richard Hamilton, artist

Dr Karl Harrison, chemist, University of Oxford
Explore interactively the nano world of chemical structures. See the molecules behind the scientific names. The website 3DChem brings colourful artworks and interactive imagery to the internet. Common chemical and medicines are presented in colourful displays along with the ability to change views, spin, zoom and fly around these molecules in 3D.

Dr Tim Herman, Director,
MSOE Center for BioMolecular Modeling, Milwaukee School of Engineering
In the biomolecular world, the tetrahedral geometry of carbon lies at the root of a hierarchical organization that leads from amino acids to proteins to molecular machines to living systems.
In yeast RNA polymerase, 31,806 atoms comprise 4,533 amino acids, joined together in a precise sequence to make up 13 individual proteins – each of which folds up into a precise shape, allowing the spontaneous assembly into the molecular machine that synthesizes messenger RNA from DNA. The determination of the molecular structure of yeast RNA polymerase was recognized by the 2006 Nobel Prize in chemistry, awarded to Roger Kornberg, Stanford University.

Helen Hignell, Department of Earth Sciences, University of Cambridge
Each type of mineral, for example diamond or calcite, displays a unique assemblage of atoms within the unit cell (the "building block" of the crystal). In the Department of Earth Sciences, building and using models helps students and researchers visualise crystal structures in 3-D while demonstrating the importance of geometry in determining the infinitely repeating pattern of atoms.

Eva Hild, sculptor

Prof. Martin Hyland, mathematician, Head of Department and Professor in Mathematical Logic, University of Cambridge
The 19th century was an extraordinary period in the history of geometry, featuring revolutionary work by giants of geometry (such as Plucker, Riemann, Klein and Lie), but also suffering from fragmentation and a lack of consensus about what should be studied and how it should be studied. One line of inquiry, pursued with great enthusiasm from the middle of the 19th century through the beginning of the 20th century, was the investigation and classification of cubic and quartic surfaces. The discovery of the existence of 27 lines on a smooth cubic surface was hailed as a discovery of monumental importance and hundreds of papers were written about cubic surfaces and their lines. Quartic surfaces emerged originally from optics and were vigorously studied by Kummer, Klein, and many others. During many of these investigations, models were built to illustrate properties of these surfaces. The construction and study of plaster models was especially popular in Germany (particularly in Gottingen under the influence of Felix Klein). Models were built of many other types of surfaces as well, including surfaces arising from the study of differential geometry and calculus.

Prof. Sir Aaron Klug, molecular biologist, Nobel Laureate – Chemistry 1982, MRC Laboratory of Molecular Biology, University of Cambridge
Aaron Klug was one of the first people, in collaboration with others, to use a combination of X-ray diffraction and electron microscopy to study the structures of macromolecules. He helped to provide the intellectual framework for understanding the self-assembly of regular viruses and developed methods for analyzing their three-dimensional structures from electron microscope images, as well as the structures of helical polymers. He and his co-workers established the basic features of chromatin organization, including the structure of the repeating units (nucleosomes) and how they are stacked together. He studied a variety of molecules that interact with DNA or RNA, including discs of tobacco mosaic virus protein, a tRNA and a ribozyme, and also discovered the zinc-finger motif in nucleic acid-binding proteins. Thus, he has played a major part in developing

the ideas and techniques that established structural molecular biology as an exciting new science during the second half of the twentieth century.

Dr Kevin Knowles, material scientist, University of Cambridge
Geometry is widely used in the field of crystallography to show the spatial arrangement of atoms in crystalline materials. Thus, for example, the crystal structure of salt, NaCl, can be described in terms of repeating blocks known as unit cells within which the sodium and chlorine ions are arranged in a fixed spatial arrangement. Ball-and-stick models can show this spatial arrangement conveniently. In such models the centres of ions or atoms are represented by small balls and adjacent ion/atom centres are joined by sticks. More complex structures such as that of DNA deduced by Crick and Watson in Cambridge in the early 1950s, in which there is a double helix, have also been famously constructed in terms of ball-and-stick models.

Langlands & Bell, artists

Steve Laurie, collections assistant, Mineralogy and Petrology, Sedgwick Museum of Earth Sciences, University of Cambridge

Bob Law, artist

George Henry Longly, artist

Dr Alan Mackay, crystallographer, (formerly) Birkbeck College, London
One of the major questions that preoccupied J. D. Bernal was the structure of water which would explain its most anomalous properties, essential for life on Earth. Why is it liquid? Bernal thought (in 1956) that the arrangement of water molecules might be icosahedral because this symmetry could not occur in crystals. He pondered on this idea sketching possibilities. He has turned out to be partly correct, but the structure of water is still a very difficult problem not yet completely understood. However, the icosahedral configuration has appeared as a key feature in many other materials (virus particles, quasi-crystals).

Kenneth Martin, artist

Josiah McElheny, artist

Dr Allan McRobie, engineer, University of Cambridge
Despite the rectilinear nature of most buildings, their stability is governed by the curved geometry of underlying smooth energy surfaces in abstract spaces. The description of such shapes is best accomplished using Catastrophe Theory, and is applicable in fields as diverse as gravitational lensing in astronomy and the appreciation of the nude in art. The beautiful patterns created by light reflecting from naturally curved surfaces is thus inextricably interlinked with the reasons why buildings collapse.

Tatsuo Miyajima, artist

Keith Moore, archivist, Head of Library and Information Services, Royal Society, London

Robert Morris, artist

Sarah Morris, artist

Dr Alex Moulton, engineer, Alex Moulton Bicycles
A bicycle frame is the main component of a bicycle, onto which wheels and other components are fitted. The modern and most common frame design for an upright bicycle is based on the safety bicycle, and is made of two triangles, a main triangle and a paired rear triangle. This is known as the diamond frame. The length of the tubes, and the angles at which they are attached define a frame geometry. In comparing different frame geometries, designers often compare the seat tube angle, head tube angle, top tube length, and seat tube length. The geometry of the frame depends on the intended use. For instance, a road bicycle will place the handlebars in a lower and further position relative to the saddle giving a more crouched riding position; whereas a utility bicycle emphasizes comfort and has higher handlebars resulting in an upright riding position. Frame geometry also affects handling characteristics.
In the late 1950s, disillusioned with the design of the classic bicycle, Alex Moulton set about creating a new design. He believed the classic diamond frame was inconvenient to mount, difficult to adjust for size, and not suitable for both sexes. Later Moulton bikes incorporate a Flexitor front suspension, and a rear suspension based on the unified rear triangle principle.

Joshua Nall, museum assistant, Whipple Museum of the History of Science, University of Cambridge

David Nash, sculptor

Carsten Nicolai, artist
"... to imagine an individual soul in each and any starlet of snow is utterly absurd, and therefore the shapes of snowflakes can by no means be deduced from the operation of a soul in the same way as in plants."
Johannes Kepler, 1611.
On entering the laboratory-like space, visitors are invited to initiate the process of growing a snow

crystal. Cooling units provide the opportunity to cool down specially prepared glass cylinders to a temperature of minus 25 degree celsius. Only a few minutes after the glass has been placed into the cooling unit, the formation of simple snow crystal structures can be observed. In the course of time, increasingly complex structures develop, none of which repeat. A systematic survey of the tremendous variety of snow crystals in the form of a diagram helps the visitor to identify individual crystal structures. Through a very subtle light and sound design snow noise focuses on micro-structures shifting the focus of our perception.

Prof. John Parker, plant scientist,
Director, Botanic Gardens, University of Cambridge

Eric Parry, architect, Eric Parry Architects
The pavilion at St Martin-in-the-Fields is one of two visible new manifestations of a large and complex transformation of the site, centred on the James Gibbs church, but also incorporating a surrounding site equivalent in area to 14 tennis courts. The pavilion is the entry into a subterranean set of spaces and will be used by around a million people a year.
The underlying pentagonal and circular geometries are informed by proportions, materials and construction which are themselves powerful voices in the synthesis. The question of geometry and cultural meaning in the context of an intense contemporary urban situation and the historical continuity of architectural debate set the process of design.

Prof. Sir Roger Penrose, mathematical physicist, Emeritus Rouse Ball Professor of Mathematics, University of Oxford
The purpose of Roger Penrose's hand-drawn diagrams is to describe as clearly as possible our present understanding of the physical universe and convey a feeling for its deep beauty and philosophical implications, as well as its intricate logical interconnections and underlying mathematical theory.

Peter Peri, artist

John Pickering, artist
The original object for this structure was a corrugated cone with a sine wave profile inversed with respect to a point not lying on the cone. A plane rotated from the main horizontal plane and passing through the centre of inversion intersects the corrugated cone and its cylclide. This part of the cyclide is subjected to a diminishing and expanding transformation with a ratio of 2:1 as an expression of cosmic flow. The centre of inversion remains at its original fixed position.

Dr Richard Preece, malacologist,
Watson Curator of Malacology, University Museum of Zoology, University of Cambridge
Directionally asymmetric animals generally exhibit no variation in handedness of whole-body architecture. In contrast, reversed chirality in both coil and entire anatomy has frequently evolved in snails. Reversed coiling inhibits interchiral mating in species with flat-shells, which mate reciprocally face-to-face so preventing the union of genitalia exposed by a sinistral on its left side with those exposed by a dextral on its right. Species with tall, slender shells mate nonreciprocally so that the 'male' copulates by mounting the 'female's' shell, mutually aligned in the same direction. This sexual asymmetry permits interchiral copulation with small behavioural adjustments. Examination of the occurrence of reversed coiling in snails indicates that reverse coiling persists for longer in populations of tall-shelled species, where selection against reversed coiling is less intense.

Dr Gareth Rees, natural scientist,
Scott Polar Institute, University of Cambridge
Stereographic projection of the Earth onto a dodecahedron. The use of the dodecahedron, one of the five Platonic Solids, represents a compromise between the distortion inherent in mapping the Earth's surface onto a single plane, and the difficulty of printing onto a sphere. The background image is a simple representation of the Earth's main vegetation zones.

Prof. Simon Schaffer, historian,
Department of the History and Philosophy of Science, University of Cambridge

Shoji Sadao, architect
Shoji Sadao collaborated with both R. Buckminster Fuller and Isamu Noguchi on many important projects. Sadao met Fuller while studying architecture at Cornell University, and it was Fuller who introduced him to Noguchi. Shoji Sadao began working with Fuller in 1954, and in 1965 formed Fuller and Sadao, P.C., whose first project was the large geodesic dome for the U.S. Pavilion at EXPO 67 in Montreal.

David Saunders, fashion designer, DavidDavid
David Saunders studied painting at Chelsea College of Art and Design. He found that symmetric geometric pattern was greatly complemented by motion and chose fashion and fabrics as a new canvas and a perfect vehicle to drive this notion.

Conrad Shawcross, artist

Dr Daina Taimina, mathematician,
Cornell University, NY
I made my first crocheted model of the hyperbolic plane in 1997 when I needed it for teaching

a geometry class at Cornell University. Since then I have been experimenting with this form, eventually making these objects more like fibre arts sculptures. It has been very interesting for me to explore the hyperbolic plane, making them with different radii, in different materials, and with different colours. It is like doing research; but the main tool is a crochet hook. For exploring different forms of the hyperbolic plane, I start with a shape I call the symmetric hyperbolic plane. I make this form following a mathematically calculated pattern in which the number of stitches in each row increases exponentially; that ensures the resulting surface has constant negative curvature (a necessary requirement for the hyperbolic plane). In two dimensions there are three geometries possible – plane geometry (no curvature), spherical geometry (constant positive curvature) and hyperbolic geometry. Once the basic shape is finished, the fun part of sculpting can start. The same basic shape can be turned in many different forms, on all of them the same hyperbolic geometry can be defined.

Keith Tyson, artist

Dr Piers Vitebsky, Head of Anthropology and Russian Northern Studies, Scott Polar Research Institute
A reindeer herder's hand-drawn map from the Nenets Okrug in the Russian Arctic. The outline corresponds very closely to the contours of an official map, but the features shown within the outline reflect the herders' own indigenous knowledge and use of the land, and would not appear on any map drawn by outsiders.

Dr Tennie Videler, chemist, University of Cambridge
Proteins are too small for their structures to be visible, even using the strongest microscope. Yet scientists have gained much experimental information on their structure. This gives atomic models, shown here as a "ribbon diagram". Scientists use these to design experiments and explain biological data. They are also extraordinarily beautiful.

Jane Wess, curator of mathematics, Science Museum, London

Father Magnus Wenninger, mathematician and monk, St John's Abbey, Collegeville, MN
It should be of special interest for mathematics students and teachers to see and handle these geometrical objects in aesthetically pleasing models and to be delighted with their beauty and form. It is surprising how the models can stimulate interest in some of the basic theorems of solid geometry.

Hugh Whitehead, Project Director, and his team, Specialist Modelling Group, Foster + Partners
In 1998 Foster + Partners set up the Specialist Modelling Group, whose brief is to carry out research and development in an environment which is intensely project driven. This challenge has given the original degree thesis a new significance. Computing technology has now come of age and in the digital era the techniques are taking on a new relevance.
Recent projects include the SwissRe Headquarters and the new City Hall in London. Hugh Whitehead's principal interest in computational design tools is the integration of analysis routines with geometry control mechanisms.
*The Specialist Modelling Group have been working with artist **John Pickering** to produce a series of experimental models especially for "Beyond Measure".*

published to accompany the exhibition

Beyond Measure: conversations across art and science

Kettle's Yard, University of Cambridge

5 April - 1 June 2008

exhibition organised by Barry Phipps with Lizzie Fisher
catalogue designed by Paul Allitt, printed by C3imaging, Colchester
© Kettle's Yard, Barry Phipps and the contributors 2008

ISBN 978 1 904561 26 2

This exhibition and related events supported by
The Henry Moore Foundation, NESTA, and Arts Council England.

Barry Phipps' Interdisciplinary Fellowship at Kettle's Yard supported by
The Isaac Newton Trust

Kettle's Yard is grant-aided by Arts Council England East,
The Arts and Humanities Research Council,
The Friends of Kettle's Yard and Cambridge City Council.

This and other Kettle's Yard publications are available from:
Kettle's Yard, Castle St, Cambridge, CB3 0AQ
tel +44 (0)1223 352124 • www.kettlesyard.co.uk